Michael Jacques

Rondino

for
Alto Saxophone
and
Piano

G. RICORDI & CO., (LONDON) LTD.

The Bury, Church Street, Chesham, Bucks.

Michael Jacques

for Alison

RONDINO

for Alto Saxophone and Piano

ALTO SAXOPHONE in E♭

Scherzando (♩ = 120)

Processed and printed by
Halstan & Co. Ltd., Amersham, Bucks., England

Michael Jacques

Rondino

for
Alto Saxophone
and
Piano

RICORDI

Michael Jacques

for Alison

RONDINO
for Alto Saxophone and Piano

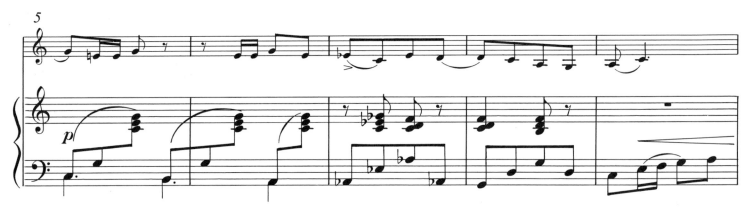

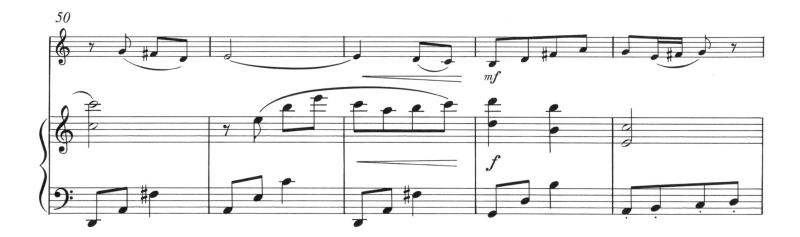

Processed and printed by
Halstan & Co. Ltd., Amersham, Bucks., England